KEY STAGE 1/P1-3

PSHE

••••• and Citizenship •••••

Clare Rowland • Teresa Woulfe

Published by Evans Brothers Limited
2A Portman Mansions
Chiltern Street
London W1M 1LE

First published 2001

© Evans Brothers Limited 2001

Typeset and designed by Raynor Design
Illustrations by Raynor Design

Rowland, Clare
  PSHE for Key Stage 1
  1.Social skills - Study and teaching (Elementary) - Great
  Britain 2.Health education (Elementary) - Great Britain
  3.Citizenship - Study and teaching (Elementary) - Great
  Britain
  I.Title II.Woulfe, Teresa
  372.8'3'044'0941

  ISBN 0237522446

Printed in Hong Kong by Dah Hua Printing Press Co., Ltd.

Contents

Introduction

The importance of PSHE and Citizenship

With the introduction of the National Curriculum 2000, the importance of PSHE and Citizenship is re-emphasised.

"Personal, Social and Health Education and Citizenship help to give pupils the knowledge, skills and understanding they need to lead confident, healthy, independent lives and to become informed, active, responsible citizens."

The 1988 Education Reform Act states that all children are entitled to receive a broad and balanced curriculum. It is vital that this curriculum prepares them for the problems they will face in adult life. A structured PSHE and Citizenship programme gives children the opportunity to understand their responsibilities as citizens within a community, to respect the lives and beliefs of others and to take responsibility for their own lives as far as they are able.

Schools that value PSHE and Citizenship give their pupils the chance to access these important areas:

- Children will recognise their own worth.
- Children will become responsible for their own learning, working collaboratively with others.
- Children will reflect upon their own experiences and learn from them.
- Children will explore many spiritual, moral, social and cultural issues.
- Children will consider their responsibilities both as individuals and members of communities.
- Children will learn to acknowledge and respect differences and similarities between people.

When children join a school they already bring with them a wealth of knowledge. They may well have firmly entrenched opinions about their own health and safety. They may well have an awareness of what they feel is right and wrong, fair and unfair, both for themselves and others. As facilitators of education we must utilise this knowledge fully. The opinions and experiences that children already have need to be addressed, sometimes challenged but never ignored.

Central to all PSHE and Citizenship work is the enhancement of self-esteem. Through a structured programme of activities, pupils will have opportunities to consider the things they have learned successfully as individuals or in groups. They will have the chance for their achievements, however small, to be recognised and rewarded. Most importantly, they will be able to express their own ideas in a climate where all opinions are given the value that they deserve. The ultimate aim is to raise every child's self-esteem which, in turn, will lead to more responsible attitudes and behaviour later in life.

How to use this book

This book is a practical and comprehensive resource specifically written to fulfill the National Curriculum requirements for the teaching of PSHE and CITIZENSHIP at Key Stage 1. The eight modules correspond closely to the requirements for knowledge, skills and understanding as outlined in the most recent curriculum guidelines:

Module 1 – Feeling Good
Children are given the opportunity to think about both their own strengths and the strengths of others. They learn how to set simple goals.

Module 2 – Making Choices
Children are encouraged to recognise real choices they can make and to differentiate between right and wrong, fair and unfair.

Module 3 – Belonging to a Family
Children consider their roles as part of a family, school and community.

Module 4 – Staying Healthy
Children are shown how to make simple choices to improve their health and well-being. They consider both their diet and their lifestyle.

Module 5 – Keeping Clean
Children learn about the importance of maintaining personal hygiene and the dangers of germs.

Module 6 – Being Safe
Children consider ways to keep safe both at home and at school. They also learn basic road safety.

Module 7 – Having Friends
Children are encouraged to recognise how their behaviour affects other people and to respect the differences between people.

Module 8 – Beating Bullies
Children consider different types of teasing and bullying and develop strategies to help them deal with bullying behaviour.

Each module has six photocopiable pupil activity sheets. These sheets are written as child-centred, active learning resources encouraging the development of pupil participation across a range of skills and activities. To accompany each activity sheet there is a structured lesson plan with extension activities to encourage children to undertake further personal work.

The activities are carefully differentiated, each one having ideas for support for children with a range of Special Educational Needs. Teachers are well aware of the diversity of development of children at Key Stage 1. They may find it helpful to use certain activity sheets selectively or to adapt them slightly. Classroom trials of the activity sheets have shown that they can also be used successfully with slightly older children.

The wide range of activities offered by the book ensures that pupils are taught the knowledge, skills and understanding through opportunities to:

- take and share responsibility
- feel positive about themselves
- take part in discussions
- make real choices
- meet and talk with people
- develop relationships through work and play
- consider social and moral dilemas
- ask for help

The following table will give guidance to teachers by showing which specific areas from the curriculum guidelines for PSHE and Citizenship each chapter is aiming to target.

Links to National Curriculum PSHE and Citizenship

Module 1 Feeling Good

1d – to think about themselves, learn from their experiences and recognise what they are good at
1e – how to set simple goals
1c – to recognise, name and deal with their feelings in a positive way
2a – to take part in discussions with one other person and the whole class
5b – feel positive about themselves

Module 2 Making Choices

1a – recognise what they like and dislike, what is fair and unfair and what is right and wrong
1b – share opinions on things that matter to them and explain their views
2b – take part in a simple debate about topical issues
2c – recognise choices they can make and recognise the difference between right and wrong
5a – take and share responsibility
5d – make real choices

Module 3 Belonging to a Family

2d – agree to follow rules for their group and classroom
2e – realise that people and other living things have needs, and that they have responsibilities to meet them
2f – that they belong to various groups and communities
2g – what improves and harms their local, natural and built environments
2h – to contribute to the life of the class and school
5g – consider social and moral dilemmas

Module 4 Staying Healthy

3a – how to make simple choices that improve their health and well-being
5b – feel positive about themselves
5d – make real choices

Module 5 Keeping Clean

3b – maintain peronal hygiene
3c – how some diseases spread and can be controlled
3d – processes of growing from young to old and how people's needs change
3e – the names of the main parts of the body
3f – all household products can be harmful if not used properly

Module 6 Being Safe

3f – all houshold products including medicines can be harmful
3g – rules for ways of keeping safe, including basic road safety
5e – meet and talk to people
5h – ask for help

Module 7 Having Friends

4a – recognise how their behaviour affects other people
4c – identify and respect differences and similarities between people
4d – family and friends should care for each other
5b – feel positive about themselves
5f – develop relationships

Module 8 Beating Bullies

4e – there are different types of teasing and bullying, that bullying is wrong
5c – take part in discussions
5g – consider moral dilemas

Cross-curricular links within the PSHE and Citizenship framework

Module 1 Feeling Good

En 1 Speaking and listening: 1d, 1f, 2a, 3a, 8d, 9a,10b.
En 2 Reading: 1f, 1n,
En 3 Writing: 1c, 1e, 2a, 4c, 4e, 4h, 5h, 10, 12

Module 2 Making Choices

En 1 Speaking and listening: 1d, 1f, 2c, 3a, 3c, 3d,4a, 10b,11 b
En 2 Reading: 1b, 1g, 3e, 7b
En 3 Writing: 1c, 1e, 2a, 4a, 2g 5h
Ma 3 Shape,space and measures: 4a

Module 3 Belonging to a Family

En 1 Speaking and listening: 1d, 1e, 2c, 2d, 3a, 3c
En 2 Reading: 1m, 2a, 2b
En 3 Writing: 1b, 1c, 1d, 4a, 5h
Sc 2 Life processes and living things: 2b, 2e, 5c
Gg: 1c, 5a, 5b

Module 4 Staying Healthy

En 1 Speaking and listening: 2c, 2d, 3a, 3c
En 2 Reading: 1a, 1b, 1c, 1h
En 3 Writing: 2a, 4a, 4b, 4c
Sc 2 Life processes and living things: 2b, 2c
P.E: 4a

Module 5 Keeping Clean

En 1 Speaking and listening: 1b, 1f, 3a, 3b
En 2 Reading: 2a, 2b, 2c, 7a
En 3 Writing: 1b, 1c, 1e, 2a, 4g, 12
Art: 5a, 5b
Sc 2 Life processes and living things: 2a, 2f
His. Chronological understanding: 1a, 1b

Module 6 Being Safe

En 1 Speaking and listening: 2a, 2b, 3a, 3c
En 2 Reading: 2a, 2c, 3b, 3d, 3e
En 3 Writing: 1b, 1c, 2a, 4g, 5h, 12
Sc 2 Life processes and living things: 2d
Mu: 1a, 1c, 2a, 2b

Module 7 Having Friends

En 1 Speaking and listening: 3a, 3b, 8d, 10b
En 2 Reading: 1j, 1n, 2a, 2b
En 3 Writing: 1a, 1e, 2a, 4e, 4g, 4h
Sc 2 Life processses and living things: 4a

Module 8 Beating Bullies

En 1 Speaking and listening: 2a, 2c, 2e, 3a, 3c, 3e, 4a, 11b
En 2 Reading: 1b, 1f, 1j, 3b
En 3 Writing: 1b, 1c, 4g, 12
Ma 2 Number: 5a

Fantastic friends

This activity enables the children to think about the other members of their class and to recognise that we all have different qualities and different areas in which we shine. It gives them the opportunity to think about things that other people are good at before discussing their own strengths.

Ask the children to sit in a large circle and invite them in turn to choose one other member of the class who they feel is good at something. In turn, ask them to walk and stand behind their friend and complete the words "This is _____. He/She is good at _____." If they wish to give reasons for or details about their friend's talents then encourage them to do so!

Give each child a copy of the activity sheet. Show them how to complete it using the white board or a large sheet of paper. You may like to use yourself as an example! Hair, eye colour, clothing and other features should be added to the picture before completing the writing. The children must choose first a boy from the class, then a girl.

Extension

Children who finish the activity sheet quickly and easily may like to choose one fantastic friend. Ask them to draw a picture and give all the details of their talents to include in a class book 'What a Clever Class we are!'

Ideas for SEN Support

You may wish to provide some children with words to choose from for eye and hair colour. Others may find it easier to draw a picture for the *he/she is good at* part of the activity sheet.

Talent tree

This activity encourages children to think about themselves in a positive way and recognise that they have many talents. It encourages them to vocalise one thing they are particularly good at and share this with others around them.

As a class teacher ask the children for ideas of what they think you are good at. Write these ideas on a white board or large sheet of paper – use one colour. Ask the children why they have chosen these attributes, what evidence do they have?

Give one example of what you are good at that the children might not know.

Using a different colour, write a couple of examples for why you are good at these particular things and perhaps who has influenced you.

Ask the children to speak to the person next to them and find out one thing that they are good at. Feed back a couple of examples to the whole class.

Ask the children to think of one thing that they think they are good at and why. Get the children to tell somebody else what this talent is.

Give feedback of a couple of examples. Why do you think you are good at this? Who or what has made you good at this?

Give each child a copy of the activity sheet. Have a larger example ready to be filled in by the teacher. Explain to the children that they will be choosing one example to write on their leaf. If the children are able they can write the reason why.

Explain to the children that all the leaves will be cut out to form a display and will be attached to a tree which celebrates things that they are good at. This tree can be a permanent display and can be added to throughout the year.

Extension

The children might use the reverse side of the leaf to write further examples. They might use two different colours as in the introduction to suggest what they are good at and why they are good at it.

Ideas for SEN Support

Using a blank leaf the children can draw one thing that they are good at and have the opportunity to write their name.

Happy moments

This activity is intended to help the children to remember happy times in their lives at home or at school. They will remember happy experiences in their lives, where they were and who they were with.

As a stimulus, share some photographs or pictures of people who look happy.

Ask the children:

- How do we know they are happy?
- Why do you think they are happy?
- Who or what has made them happy?

As a group talk about happy things that have happened to them that day or week. Discuss who or what has made them happy. Write a couple of examples on a board or large sheet of paper.

Talk about other times in their lives when something has made them happy, help the children to recognise the aspect of chronology. Brainstorm some of the ideas and record them as *today, yesterday* and *a long time ago*.

Give each child a copy of the activity sheet and ask what type of mouth needs to be drawn on to make the person happy. The children will be required to complete this.

Discuss with the children what needs to go into the think bubble. Encourage the children to use a mixture of pictures and words to show a happy moment in their lives.

Extension

As part of a homework activity the children could discuss happy moments at home or as part of a family. Examples could be given to parents such as: birth of a child, party celebration, child receiving a medal or certificate.

Ideas for SEN Support

The children should be required to think of things that make them happy and one word or phrase could be recorded. The children will draw a picture of themselves looking happy.

Happy or sad?

This activity gives the children the opportunity to look at the emotions of happiness and sadness and to discuss a variety of experiences which lead them to feel these differing emotions.

Using the board or a large piece of paper draw a happy face at the top of one side and a sad face at the top of the other. Ask the children to give examples of experiences that have made them feel happy and collect their ideas under the happy face. Repeat this brainstorming idea with the sad face. Also explore the reasons *why* some situations make us feel happy or sad.

Invite the children to complete the activity sheet individually and then return to one large group to discuss the answers that they gave. It may be particularly interesting to look at the different answers given by boys and girls. Use this as an opportunity to discuss how bottled-up feelings can make life more difficult both for the individual and those around him or her.

Extension

Invite the children to explore facial expressions that convey happiness/sadness/anger/fear. Ask one member of the group to use a book to cover his/her face and then move it slowly downwards so that only the eyes are showing. What emotion is he/she feeling? If a member of the group guesses correctly then it is their turn to be on.

Ideas for SEN Support

Some children may like to look through magazines and to cut out pictures that make them feel happy or sad. Happy pictures could be stuck on a green piece of card and sad pictures on a red piece.

Award time

This activity is intended to promote discussion about the positive qualities we see in other people. It is intended to build self-esteem of the children by sharing the qualities of others as a whole class group.

Make a collection of certificates that are used in the school. Ask children to bring in certificates that they have been awarded out of school.

Discuss why we present certificates to people. Look at the collection of certificates and try to categorise what they have been given for, e.g. sport, art.

In turn ask the children to share an example of one certificate that has been presented to them. What was it presented for? Where was it presented to you? Who was there to see it presented to you? How did it make you feel? Where do you keep it?

Select a child (perhaps one who has no recollection of receiving a certificate) and write their name on a board. Ask the rest of the class for examples of what that child could be given a certificate for. Use tangible and intangible qualities e.g. for being a good singer, for being a nice person. Repeat this with a few more children.

Tell the children that you want them to think of somebody on their table to award a certificate to. Feed back ideas to ensure that all children have been identified.

Give a copy of the activity sheet to each child and read through it, identifying what needs to be written. The teacher should demonstrate with one of the previous children used.

The children should fill in an individual certificate and maybe illustrate it with pictures that represent that person.

Extension

In a class or school assembly the children can stand up and present their certificates to each other. The emphasis is on the child speaking clearly and sharing the reason why the certificate has been presented.

Ideas for SEN Support

The teacher should work with a group and act as scribe after discussion. The children should then be prepared to present their certificates.

What a great goal!

This activity encourages the children to set themselves simple goals and to work each day towards achieving those goals. It provides a record sheet which will show their progress on a daily basis. This record can be used as part of a self-evaluation, at the end of the week giving opportunities for discussion with both the teacher and the rest of the class. In this way the children are encouraged to identify realistic and achievable goals.

As a whole class ask the children what they would like to be better at. Collect their ideas on a board or a large piece of paper. Ideas can range from school-related tasks, such as reading or times tables, to helping in the home or improving football skills. Using a few children's ideas, identify a task that could easily be done on a daily basis to help them reach their goal. Explain how the activity sheet should be filled in each day.

Give each child a copy of the activity sheet and invite them to work in pairs to discuss suitable goals and complete these at the top of the activity sheet. Ask the children to complete the activity sheet each day and to bring it back the following week.

Extension

Some children may like to complete a more formal self-evaluation. What was their goal? Did they achieve it? Were the tasks easy or hard? What targets would they choose next? etc.

Ideas for SEN support

Any children with special educational needs may like to choose a target from their Individual Educational Plan.

name . . . .

Fantastic friends

This is . . . .

He has . . . . hair

and . . . . eyes.

He is good at . . . .

. . . .

. . . .

. . . .

This is . . . .

She has . . . . hair

and . . . . eyes.

She is good at . . . .

. . . .

. . . .

. . . .

name ....

Talent tree

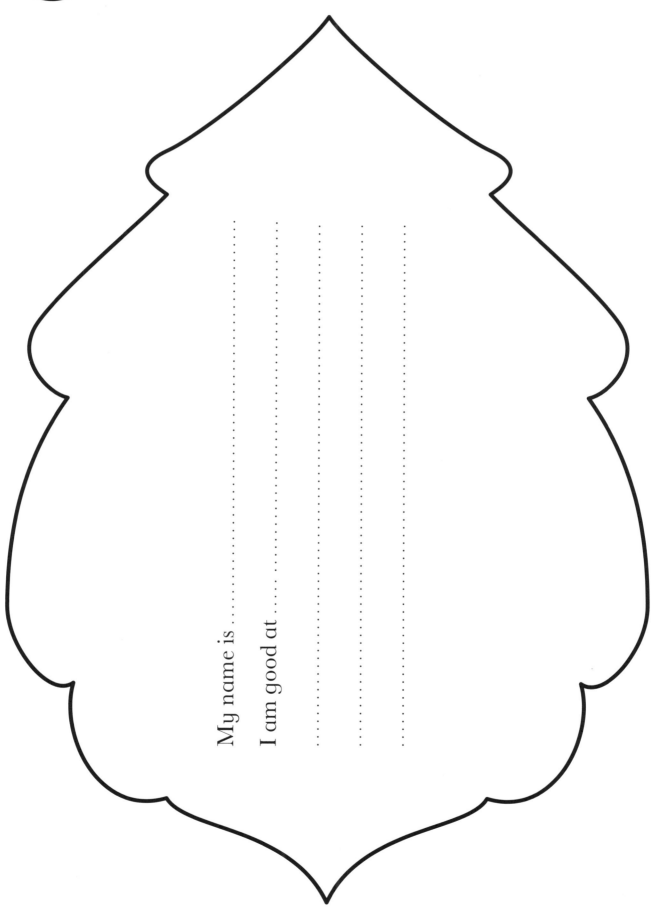

My name is ....

I am good at ....

 ACTIVITY SHEET 3

name . . . .

Happy moments

Draw a happy mouth on this person.

Draw and write about a happy time.

name . . . .

Happy or sad?

Colour the square green if you think it would make you feel happy. Colour it red if it would make you feel sad.

Now try 2 of your own:

I would feel happy because

. . . .

. . . .

I would feel sad because

. . . .

. . . .

ACTIVITY 5 SHEET

name . . . .

Award time

Certificate

This certificate is awarded to

. . . .

for

. . . .

. . . .

signed . . . . date . . . .

name ....

What a great goal!

This week I am going to

....

....

....

....

....

	Yes!	No!
Monday		
Tuesday		
Wednesday		
Thursday		
Friday		
Saturday		
Sunday		

.... completed the task each day.

Signed........................... parent/guardian

Like it or lump it!

This activity encourages children to think about the things that they like and those that they do not like. It also gives them the opportunity to take part in a class discussion and to share their opinions with others.

Ask the children to sit in a large circle and then pose the question "What do you really like to eat?" Listen to answers from children who volunteer information easily before encouraging each member of the circle to contribute. Pick some other questions such as "What do you really dislike doing at school?" and repeat the activity above. Use it as an opportunity to explain that we all have different likes and dislikes – there is no right or wrong.

Give each child a copy of the activity sheet and invite them to draw a picture in each quarter of the 'like' and 'dislike' wheels. Labels or phrases should be added if the children are confident writers.

Extension

This could be the starting point for a display in the classroom, with the different groups of children responsible for different parts on large 'like' and 'dislike' wheels.

Ideas for SEN Support

It may be useful to eliminate two of the titles on each wheel for the children with special educational needs. This gives a wheel split into two halves and thus less to think about and more space.

Where I would rather be

This activity gives the children the opportunity to think about places they would like to be. It allows them to perhaps suggest likes that are not easily available but are rather a dream or fantasy.

The teacher should start the discussion by stating "If I wasn't teaching here today, I would rather be…"

Give reasons to the children for your choices and share several examples with the children.

Ask the children to share suggestions of places where they would rather be and record a few examples on a white board or piece of paper. Encourage the children to give reasons for their choices.

As a class create a shared piece of writing – *My teacher thinks…*

Using this as a starting point the children can complete the sentence using their previous examples.

e.g. My teacher thinks I'm reading my book but I'm not, I'm on stage singing with SClub 7.

Encourage the children to be as adventurous as possible!

Give each child an activity sheet and explain how they are to be filled in. Discuss what they can draw in the think bubble, explain that it should be somewhere that they would like to be if they weren't in school. If the child is capable, they can write a sentence starting *My teacher thinks…* across the top of the think bubble. The teacher or assistant should do this for other children.

Extension

Children who finish the activity sheet can use a writing frame to write their own poem MY TEACHER THINKS. This could form part of a central display with the think bubbles around it.

Ideas for SEN Support

You might wish to provide pictures of places where the children might rather be (e.g. the beach, at the fair). They could cut these out and stick them on to their think bubble.

It's not fair!

This activity allows children to explore situations at school that are fair or unfair. They should be able to realise that everybody has a time when they feel that a child or an adult has been unfair in their dealings with them.

Distribute a copy of the poem 'It's not fair' to the children. Enlarge one copy or use as an overhead transparency. Read through the poem with the children. Ask the children who they think has written the poem, give them a couple of minutes to come up with some suggestions. Allow some feedback of ideas.

Using the poem, ask the children to identify what the different situations are e.g. verse 1 suggests children being told off for talking. Challenge the children to identify what each verse represents.

Ask the children if there are any other aspects of school life where they feel that things aren't fair and write their ideas on a board or piece of paper.

Split the class into groups and allocate a verse to each group. Ask the children to put together a short drama to represent what their verse is about. You might like to work with a group and direct them.

Allow a bit of time for each group to show their drama. Ask the children if they can think of a way to make their situation fair.

As an independent activity ask the children to illustrate one or more of the verses. Share the results at the end of the lesson and group them together in verses.

Extension

Challenge the children to write another verse to the poem based on their perception of things that are not fair.

Ideas for SEN Support

Allow the children a further opportunity to listen to the poem – a listening station would be useful. They could be given statements which they would have to categorise into fair and unfair.

All the fun of the fair!

This activity gives the children the chance to explore feelings of injustice in their own lives. It gives them the opportunity to discuss issues which they feel are both fair and unfair. It also enables them to consider possible compromises that they may have to reach with the adults who care for them.

Prepare approximately ten labels of issues that the children may consider to be fair or unfair e.g. being told off when you didn't do anything, having to go to bed at 8 o'clock, having to tidy your bedroom, helping with the washing up etc. Invite the children to sit in a circle, and put two boxes labelled *fair* and *unfair* in the centre.

Read out one label at a time and choose a child to put it in the box where they feel it belongs. As a child decides which box the label should go into they may like to give an explanation to the rest of the class for the choice they have made. "I think this would be fair/unfair because…" Reassure them that they may not always agree with one another.

As each label is put into the box, use it as an opportunity to discuss *why* adults may ask them to do certain things. Would they feel tired if they stayed up till midnight during the week? Is it fair for their parents to cook a meal and wash up too? Could they compromise? etc.

Invite the children to work in small mixed groups and give each group two labels from each of the *fair* and *unfair* boxes. Each child should have a copy of the activity sheet and use the labels given to their group to write the two examples of things that are fair and unfair beside the cages of the Big Wheel. Ask the children to draw a small picture to illustrate each one inside the cage and write *fair* or *unfair* in the bubble as appropriate.

Extension

Invite the more able children to think up their own examples and to fill in a separate Big Wheel with these ideas.

Ideas for SEN support

Give some children sheets that already have the labels written beside the cages. Their task is to draw a small picture inside the cage and to identify *fair* and *unfair* orally.

Right or wrong?

This activity reinforces the children's concepts of right and wrong. It also extends their vocabulary on this theme.

As a whole class ask the children what type of behaviour is acceptable or RIGHT when they are at school. Collect their ideas on the board or a large piece of paper. Repeat this activity for behaviour that is unacceptable or WRONG at school. Ensure that the words from the wordsearch are included.

Give each child a copy of the activity sheet and ask them to look at the words written around the edge and to find them in the wordsearch. Any words that describe behaviour that they feel is RIGHT should be coloured green and any words that describe behaviour that they feel is WRONG should be coloured red.

Extension

Invite the more able children to use their dictionaries to look up and note the precise meanings of the words listed. Some children may wish to make up their own wordsearch puzzles of other right and wrong behaviour.

Ideas for SEN Support

Using the National Literacy Strategy High Frequency Word list for Reception, the children may like to write some simple 'ing' words e.g. *going, looking, playing*, with a picture to illustrate each word.

Crime and punishment

This activity encourages the children to discuss the relative severity of different behaviour. It helps them to recognise the real choices that they can make between right and wrong. It also gives them the opportunity to think about the appropriateness and effectiveness of different punishments.

Invite the children to work in pairs and give each pair a copy of the activity sheet. You may wish to pair more able with less able children. Ask the children to cut up the sheet into six parts, using the dotted lines as guides. Their task is to discuss how serious each action is and then to put them in order with the least serious first and the most serious last.

Return as a whole class and compare results, highlighting the fact that some of their answers may well be different.

Extension

Invite the children to invent punishments that they think will work to prevent any recurrence of each form of behaviour. Would it be better to fine the girl dropping litter or ask her to collect litter in the playground for a week?

Ideas for SEN Support

Mixed ability groupings should ensure that all children have equal access to this activity. Children with SEN may like to choose only one punishment and then feed back orally to their group or the class. Alternatively, you may like an adult in the classroom to lead their discussion.

ACTIVITY
7
SHEET

name ....

Like it or lump it!

Things that I like...

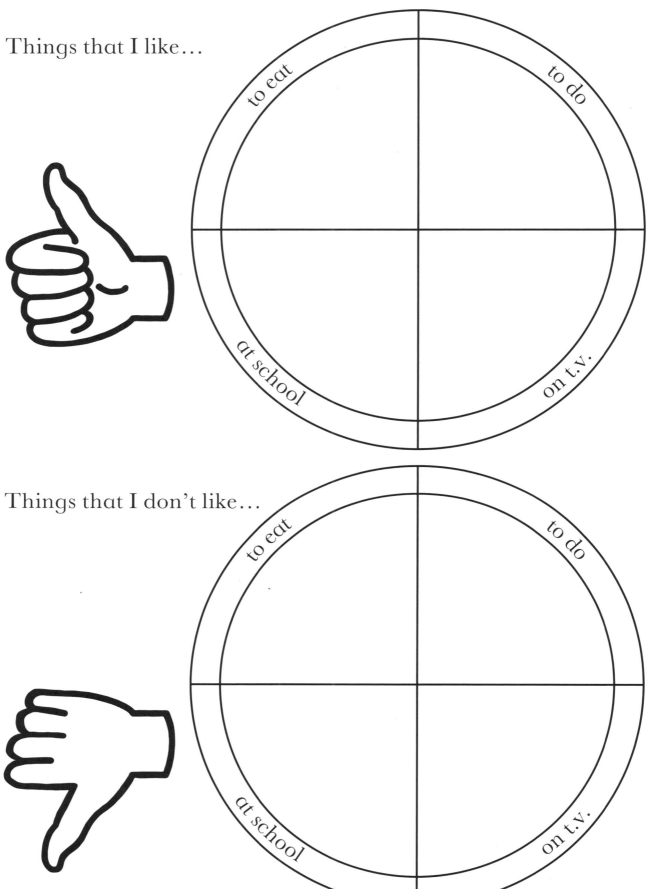

to eat

to do

at school

on t.v.

Things that I don't like...

to eat

to do

at school

on t.v.

name ....

Where I would rather be

....

....

....

2 + 9 = 11

name ....

It's not fair!

It's Not Fair

Why us? It was them not us,
They were talking and making a fuss.
It's just not fair, it's always the same,
When they do wrong but we get the blame.

That's not right, we shouldn't be here,
Please Miss, let us make it clear.
It wasn't us who started to fight,
It's just not fair, you know we're right.

Standing, watching, dying to run,
It's not fair they're all having fun.
Let me kick it please, just one time,
I really wish that ball was mine.

She pushed in front, she always does,
And no-one seems to notice because
She's bigger than me and clever too,
Because she always smiles at you.

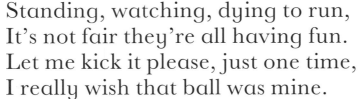

Life would be easy if school was fair,
And Miss could see that I really care.
I just want her to stop and see,
That when things go wrong, it's not always me!

Teresa Woulfe

All the fun of the fair!

Can you think of two things that are fair?

Can you think of two things that are unfair?

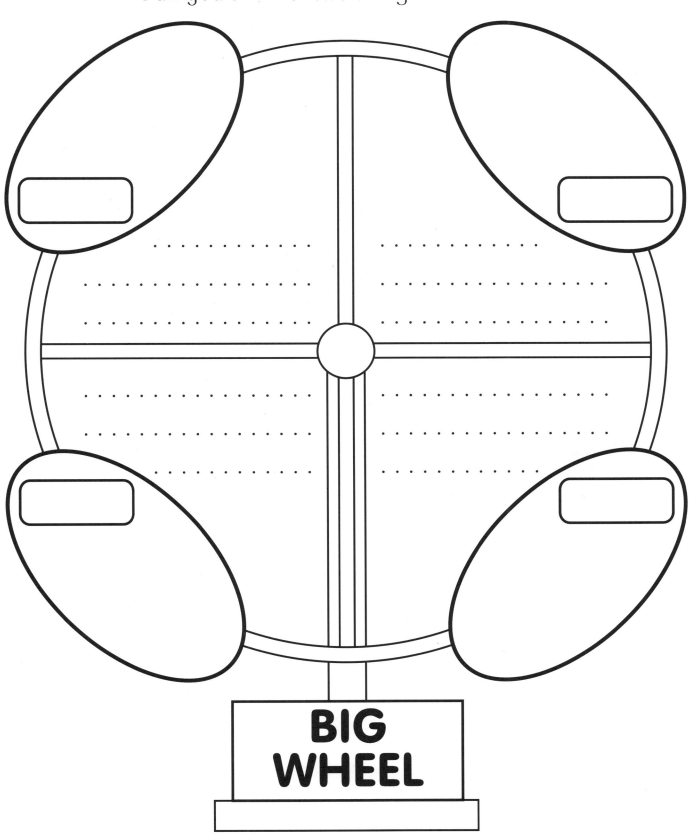

Right or wrong?

Can you find the words and colour them in?

Green = **right**　　　　　　　Red = **wrong**

teasing

fighting

shouting out

a	l	c	j	b	z	x	m	c	o	b	p
w	o	r	k	i	n	g		h	a	r	d
a	s	t	e	a	l	i	n	g	e	a	o
s	m	e	a	l	b	x	a	z	e	b	r
h	s	a	m	c	o	z	l	t	c	h	f
a	a	s	j	b	a	k	l	a	m	e	o
r	f	i	g	h	t	i	n	g	c	l	t
i	f	ń	a	c	j	l	b	m	c	p	b
n	z	g	r	a	o	f	a	t	h	i	m
g	l	b	s	t	r	b	f	g	l	n	m
o	a	l	i	s	t	e	n	i	n	g	b
e	s	l	c	a	f	g	a	c	a	r	k
s	h	o	u	t	i	n	g		o	u	t
a	x	a	f	b	g	c	m	c	b	k	l

listening

helping

stealing

sharing

working hard

24

name . . . .

Crime and punishment

stealing money

dropping litter

forgetting your homework

breaking into cars

doing graffiti

shoplifting

My family

This activity is intended to give the children the opportunity to look at the relationships that they have with members of their family. It encourages them to think about how their family help them and also to look at the responsibilities that they themselves have.

As a whole class discuss who might be a member of their family e.g. mum, dad, brother, sister, cat, dog. Remember to include different types of families that exist such as: single-parent families, families with fostered and adopted children, families with grandparents, families with step-parents and children who may be in care.

Invite the children to complete the activity sheet by drawing five members of their family and writing their names underneath. Divide the children into pairs or small groups and ask them to discuss the questions

1 How do members of your family help you?
2 In what ways do you help them?

Extension

As a circle time activity invite the children to say 'The most important person in my family is _____. I help him/her by _____.'

Ideas for SEN Support

Photocopy the activity sheet on to card and cut out four windows for each child. Invite them to complete each window as above. The cards can be used to play Happy Families or Family Snap to develop turn-taking skills.

Looking after my pet

This activity helps the children to realise that living things have needs and that we all have responsibilities to meet those needs. It encourages them to take or share this responsibility for looking after their pets well.

As a whole class activity ask the children to respond to 'My pet is a _____. It is called _____.'

As each child answers, make a tally of different kinds of pets on the board or a large piece of paper. Remember to include the category of 'no pets'!

Ask the children what types of jobs they have to do to keep their pet happy and healthy. What would be the repercussions if they didn't do this?

Divide the children into groups so that they are sitting with others who have the same type of pet. If some do not have a pet you may like to use a classroom pet or a cyber-pet! Give each child a copy of the activity sheet to complete, encouraging the more able to give more details.

Extension

The children may like to use the information on the tally chart to produce bar graphs showing the pets belonging to their class. If you are brave, you may wish to have a pet day when children bring in their pets to show everyone. Certificates could be awarded for pets that are well looked after.

Ideas for SEN Support

The mixed ability groups should help some children in the class. Pictorial answers can be given if preferred.

Membership card

This activity gives the children the opportunity to think about different groups that they belong to. It enables them to consider both the aims and rules of these groups and to discuss emblems and their meanings.

Ask the children to bring in sweatshirts/t-shirts for any groups that members of their family belong to e.g. play group, Cubs, Brownies, dance group. Make a display of the tops at the front of the classroom.

As a whole class start by looking at an emblem that the children are all familiar with – perhaps the school sweatshirt. What does the emblem look like? Does it convey a meaning? Look at all the emblems, asking for the children's opinions on their suitability for the group that they represent.

Give each child a copy of the activity sheet, which has been photocopied on to card. Invite them to design a membership card for any group they wish with an appropriate emblem on the front. The children can choose a group they are already part of e.g. their own family, Rainbows etc. or a group they would like to form e.g. a science club or a fan club for a pop star.

Extension

Invite the children to discuss rules that would help their group and to write these rules inside their membership cards.

Ideas for SEN Support

Some children may like to feed their rules back orally to the group. Alternatively they could draw pictures of activities for the group inside their card.

Go to the top of the class!

This activity is intended to consolidate the children's concepts of acceptable behaviour within the classroom. It helps them to understand how rules can help them.

Reinforce the RIGHT and WRONG behaviour that the children discussed as part of Activity Sheet 11. Collect the RIGHT behaviour on the board or a large piece of paper and clarify the importance of rules that enable groups to function well.

Divide the children into small mixed groups. Give each group a copy of the activity sheet, if possible enlarged to A3 size beforehand. Each player will need a coloured counter and each group will need a dice.

Play commences with the roll of the dice, the players moving their counters accordingly and following the instructions on the game. The winner is the player who reaches the top of the class first!

Extension

Some children may wish to colour in a large copy of the game that has been photocopied on to card. The completed game can be laminated and then kept as a classroom resource.

Ideas for SEN Support

You may wish to supervise one group to help children who have difficulties with turn-taking or who are unable to read the text. This would also give the children the opportunity to discuss the importance of classroom rules in a small group where they may feel more confident to express their opinions.

School rules

This activity gives the children in each class the opportunity to contribute to the life of the school by negotiating and following rules for their own school.

Reinforce the classroom rules that were discussed as part of Activity Sheet 16. Now ask the children for their ideas for rules for the whole school. Collect these ideas on the board or a large piece of paper. Negotiate with the children to pick out four rules which apply to all classes and can be observed throughout the day e.g.:

1 When the whistle is blown – STOP.
2 Keep your hands and feet to yourself.

Give each child a copy of the activity sheet and ask them to make their own copy of the agreed set of four rules. Explain that each class in the school will be presenting their ideas to the Head Teacher before the final four are chosen.

Extension

Divide the class into four groups and ask each group to cut out one of the rules. Firstly, using role play, they should show what would happen if they did not keep to the rule and then show the difference if they did keep to the rule. Invite other children to design posters to be placed around the school with 'Cool Schools Keep to the Rules' as the central logo.

Ideas for SEN Support

It may be more appropriate for some of the children to use symbols for each rule e.g. a picture of a whistle and a STOP sign to depict rule

1 When the whistle is blown – STOP.

The environment

This activity allows the children to explore their own environment and to realise that they have a duty towards looking after it and keeping it clean.

Discuss the range of environments that there are, e.g. school, home, town, city, country. Develop the idea that some of these environments are natural and some are man-made. Also develop the idea that some of these environments exist only for humans, some exist only for animals and some exist for both.

Ask the children which environment they know the best. For example, home – who looks after this environment and what do they do to help look after it?

Repeat this activity with the school environment – who looks after this environment and what do they do to help look after it?

Invite the children to talk about their local environment and how it is affected by people not looking after it. If appropriate and if possible you might like to take the children on a short walk around their local area, making a note or taking photographs of things that are harming their environment. Again discuss who is responsible for keeping their local area clean and what can they do to help.

Give each child a copy of the activity sheet. Discuss the situations and ask what can be done to keep the environment clean and healthy. Explain that they are going to show how the situations can be reversed or controlled.

Extension

Some children might like to make a list of rules to keep the school environment clean and healthy.

Ideas for SEN Support

The children might like to design posters to try and keep the school environment clean e.g. Don't drop litter.

name . . . .

My family

Draw a picture of a member of your family in each window and write his or her name underneath.

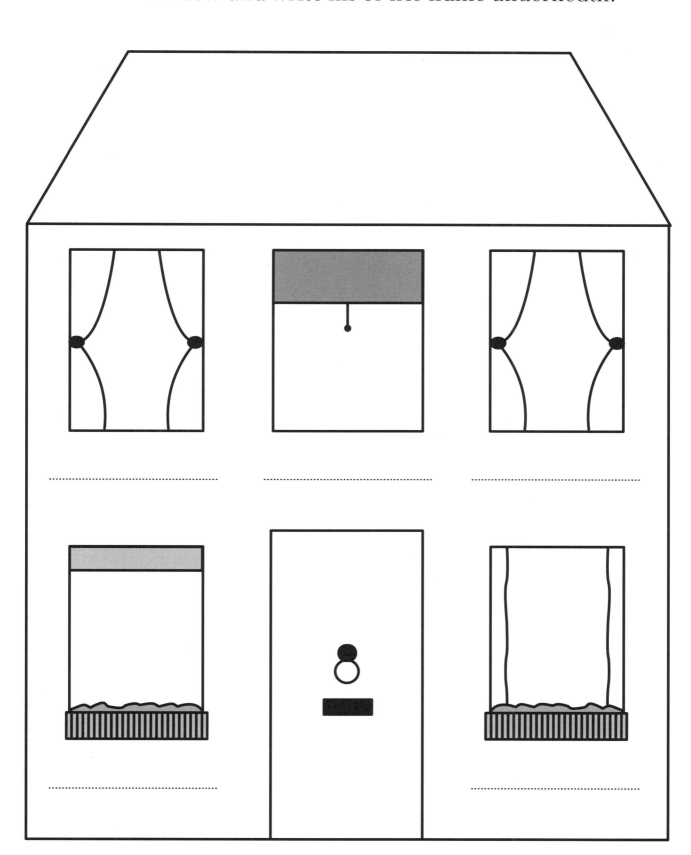

name . . . .

Looking after my pet

This is my pet called

. . . .

My pet is a

. . . .

My pet likes to eat

. . . .

. . . .

My pet lives in

. . . .

. . . .

For exercise my pet likes to

. . . .

. . . .

ACTIVITY
15
SHEET

name ....

Membership card

Cut along the dotted line then fold in half.

✂ ···

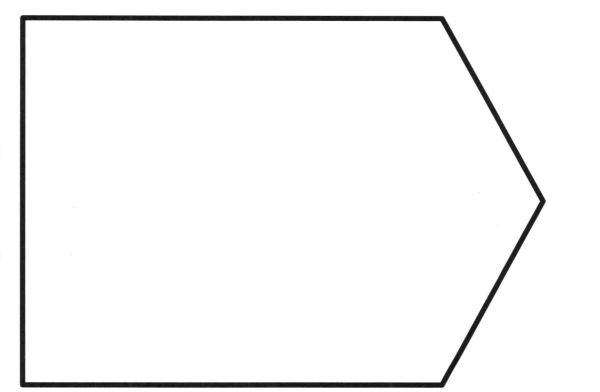

MEMBERSHIP
CARD

ACTIVITY 16 SHEET

name ....

Go to the top of the class!

Have fun playing this game!

You will need
- a counter for each player
- a dice

WELL DONE!

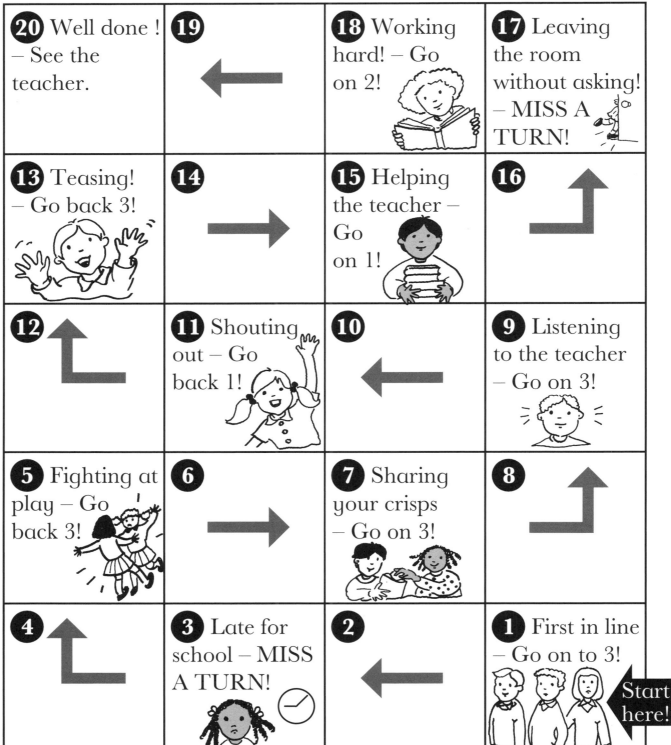

20 Well done! – See the teacher.	**19** ←	**18** Working hard! – Go on 2!	**17** Leaving the room without asking! – MISS A TURN!
13 Teasing! – Go back 3!	**14** →	**15** Helping the teacher – Go on 1!	**16** ↑
12 ↑	**11** Shouting out – Go back 1!	**10** ←	**9** Listening to the teacher – Go on 3!
5 Fighting at play – Go back 3!	**6** →	**7** Sharing your crisps – Go on 3!	**8** ↑
4 ↑	**3** Late for school – MISS A TURN!	**2** ←	**1** First in line – Go on to 3! **Start here!**

ACTIVITY SHEET 17

name . . . .

School rules

1 . . . .

. . . .

2 . . . .

. . . .

3 . . . .

. . . .

4 . . . .

. . . .

name . . . .

The environment

Draw pictures to show the environment cleaned up.

Healthy eating

This activity aims to promote discussion about healthy eating styles. It invites the children to make real choices about what they eat. It also gives the children some nutritional information on which to base their choices.

Brainstorm on the board or piece of paper what children have had for their breakfast that morning. If your school operates a breakfast club you might like to obtain a menu prior to the lesson. Ask the children who made the choices for what they ate – how different would their breakfast be if they had sole choice?

Discuss what we mean by a healthy balanced diet, and why we need to have one – for healthy skin, healthy hair, for energy etc. Talk briefly about the main food categories.

Main food groups

Proteins – meat, fish, cheese, eggs, milk, beans, nuts.

Carbohydrates – bread, pasta, rice, potatoes, biscuits, chocolates.

Vitamins and minerals – cabbage, fish, carrots, apples, oranges, milk.

Have available pictures from each group that can be placed on to 3 pieces of card – these will be needed for the independent activity.

Give each child a copy of the activity sheet. Explain that they are going to choose a healthy meal that they would like to eat that evening. Tell the children that they must try to select foods from the three groups.

Extension

The children could keep a diary for a day of what they have eaten – parents should help with this. These can be discussed to find out who is a healthy eater and who is not! Teachers should be sensitive to difficult home situations.

Ideas for SEN Support

You might like to provide extra pictures for children who have difficulty with drawing and writing to stick on to their plate. They should then be encouraged to talk about their choices to a small group or the rest of the class.

Fruit or veg?

This activity teaches the children about different types of fruit and vegetables. It also encourages them to make choices to improve their diet.

Bring a variety of fruit and vegetables to show the children, making sure that you include all the types on the activity sheet. Some children may not have seen all of them in their raw state before! Ask the children to give you the correct names for the fruit and vegetables and list them on the board or a large piece of paper. Discuss which are fruits and which are vegetables – don't forget that the tomato is a fruit! Also discuss why fresh fruit and vegetables are good for us.

Give each child a copy of the activity sheet and ask them to complete the names and also to fill in the boxes with 'F' for fruit and 'V' for vegetables. They can use the list on the board to help them. Invite them to complete the sheet by colouring it in using the correct coloured pencil crayons.

Extension

Some children may like to attempt sketches of the fruit and vegetables, both whole and cut in half.

Ideas for SEN Support

Photocopy the pictures on to cards and write the names of the fruit and vegetables on separate cards. The children can then try some matching and sorting activities using initial letter sounds to help them.

Chance to choose!

This activity is intended to reinforce the importance of making sensible choices about what we eat. It encourages the children to think of different types of food that begin with the phonetic blend *ch* before categorising them.

Depending on the timing of this lesson, introduce or recap on the initial blend *ch* – make a list of all offers given by the children. If any children give you final blends, accept them too!

Now ask the children if they can think of any foods that begin with the blend *ch*. Make a list if these on a board or piece of paper. Begin by asking the children if they would come under the headings *healthy* or *unhealthy*. A real challenge would be if any children can remember what food group they belong to.

Give each child a copy of the activity sheet, identify the pictures around the edge and explain how the rest of the sheet needs to be filled in. The words need to be available for the children to copy:

chocolate, cheese, chips, chicken, cherries

Extension

The children can try creating another sheet beginning with another blend e.g. *cr*

Ideas for SEN Support

The children could try another activity choosing their foods by the initial letter rather than an initial blend.

Healthy Options card game

This activity helps the children to see which leisure time pursuits are the best for them. It encourages them to make simple choices to improve their health and well-being.

Give each child an activity sheet that has been photocopied on to card, and read it with them. Invite them to colour in the illustrations and then to cut the pictures up carefully so that they each have nine cards. On the reverse of the card ask the children to put a green tick if it depicts a healthy activity that would help them to keep fit and a red cross if it depicts a more unhealthy option.

Ask the children to work in mixed groups of four. All the cards should be put together, shuffled and then dealt out. The game is played in exactly the same way as 'Happy Families' and the winner is the person who has the most complete sets of four (i.e. 4 × walking the dog, 4 × watching tv etc.).

Extension

Invite the children to work in pairs to think of other activities that would improve their health and well-being. They can make a list of as many as possible or draw pictures if this is more appropriate for their ability level.

Ideas for SEN Support

One group may like to work with a partner, deal out the cards face down and then play 'pairs'. A group discussion could follow to reinforce which activities are the healthy options and why.

Keep Fit crossword

This activity encourages the children to think about different types of physical activities that will help to develop a healthy lifestyle.

Ask the children to stand up and perform certain activities on the spot. Hold up a card which shows an activity e.g. JUMP. Ask the children to do what is on the card and only to stop when you say so. Hold up a different card e.g. WALK and repeat the activity. You should allow enough time for the children to become breathless or red-faced.

Be aware of any of the children who have breathing difficulties. Choose an appropriate activity for any child who has a disability.

Discuss what the activity has done to them and their bodies and collect ideas on a board or piece of paper. Ask the children :

- Why is it important to exercise?
- What happens to our bodies when we exercise?
- What would happen to our bodies if we didn't exercise?
- What types of exercise do you do? (This should include walking to school, playing in the playground.)

Give each child a copy of the activity sheet. Make sure that they all understand the concept of a crossword. Identify the activities and what the people are doing. Encourage the use of *walking* rather than *walk* and discuss the difference in spelling.

Extension

The children could take each verb in turn and put them into a complete sentence.

Ideas for SEN Support

The crossword could be given to the children already filled in and their task would be to link the words to the pictures.

How fit can you get?

This activity encourages the children to set simple goals to improve their health and fitness.

As part of a P.E. lesson ask the children to think of an activity that they could do in the playground or hall to improve their stamina. Let the children work in small groups or with a partner for five minutes and then feed back to the rest of the class. You may feel it necessary to guide some children in their choices e.g. running from one side to the other, doing star jumps, hopping on one leg then the other, skipping with a rope, etc.

Ask the children to work with a partner on their chosen activity whilst you time them for two or three minutes. One child should count how many times their partner achieves the chosen task whilst the other is doing it. Repeat this by swopping over so that every child has had a go.

The activity sheet is to be used as a daily record to show their progress and to encourage them to beat their personal best. The children should colour in the smiley face and fill in their total. As the class teacher, you should find a suitable period of time for the activity on a daily basis. Explain to the children that their fitness can be increased by practising during play-times or lunch hours.

Extension

Some children may like to continue the activity for a period of weeks and then discuss their results.

Ideas for SEN Support

Any child who has a disability can choose an appropriate activity.

name . . . .

Healthy eating

Plan a healthy meal that you would like to eat.

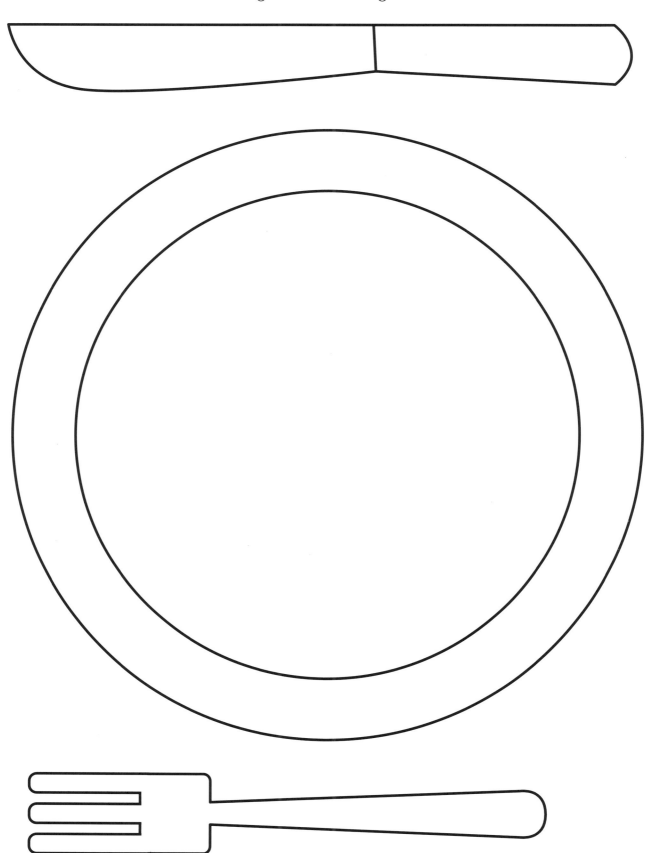

name ....

Fruit or veg?

Complete the names of the fruit and vegetables.
If it is a fruit write 'F' in the box.
If it is a vegetable write 'V'.

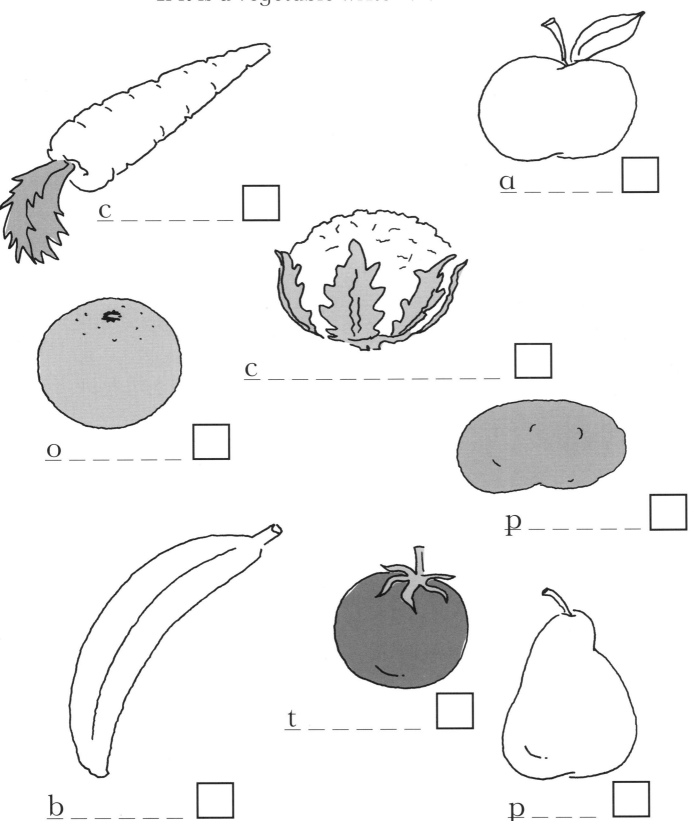

c _ _ _ _ _ ☐

a _ _ _ _ _ ☐

c _ _ _ _ _ _ _ _ _ _ ☐

o _ _ _ _ _ ☐

p _ _ _ _ _ _ ☐

b _ _ _ _ _ ☐

t _ _ _ _ _ _ ☐

p _ _ _ ☐

name ....

Chance to choose!

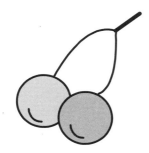

c h _ _ _ _ _ _

c h _ _ _ _ _

c h _ _ _

ch

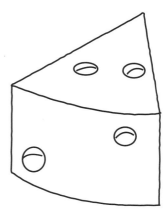

c h _ _ _ _

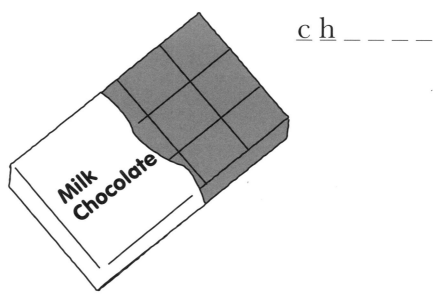

c h _ _ _ _ _ _ _ _

40

name . . . .

Healthy Options card game

Colour in your pictures. Then cut them up so that you have 9 cards ready to play the game.

Swimming

Sleeping in late

Watching tv

Playing football

Dancing at the disco

Walking the dog

Playing computer games

Cycling

Buying sweets

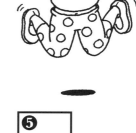

name . . . .

ACTIVITY 23 SHEET

Keep Fit crossword

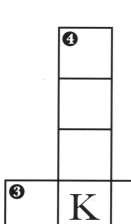

❶

❷

M

❺

N

❹

❷

❸ K

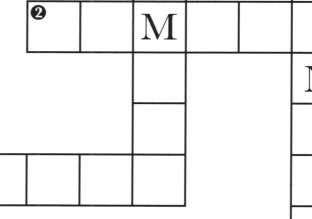

❸

❺

❹

name . . . .

ACTIVITY 24 SHEET

How fit can you get?

I am going to . . . .

for . . . . minutes every day!

Monday

I did ☐ !

Tuesday

I did ☐ !

Wednesday

I did ☐ !

Thursday

I did ☐ !

Friday

I did ☐ !

WELL DONE! YOU DID IT!

signed . . . .

(Class teacher)

Parts of the body

This activity helps the children to become familiar with the names of the main parts of the body.

Prepare an outline of a person on the board or a large piece of paper. Also prepare labels of the body parts that are on the activity sheet. Divide the children into two groups for a 'Label the parts of the body' game.

Choose a child from one team to start. They pick one of the cards and show it to their team, who can help them to read it. It is their job to stick it in the appropriate place. If they are successful they win a point. If not, the card is given to the other team.

The activity sheet serves to reinforce their knowledge. Give each child a copy of the sheet and invite them to complete the names of each part of the body. They can use the words at the bottom of the activity sheet to help them.

Extension

Divide the children into small groups. Ask one of the group to lie down on a large piece of paper and the other children to draw around them. Invite each group to paint their person and give them a few of the labels used earlier to stick on their work when it is dry. These could be exhibited as part of a wall display.

Ideas for SEN Support

With the help of an adult, some children may like to repeat the game using fewer labels. This will increase their confidence with a few parts of the body before moving to the rest if appropriate.

Can you keep clean?

This activity teaches the children which parts of the body need careful cleaning. It encourages them to maintain personal hygiene.

Prepare an outline of a person on the board or a large piece of paper. Ask the children which parts of the body need careful washing and invite them to come up and draw arrows to the body parts using a marker pen. Discuss why certain parts need to be kept very clean – spread of germs, dental decay, avoidance of 'being smelly' etc. This is a useful opportunity to address any inappropriate reactions to washing bodily parts.

Use this as an opportunity to show that cleanliness is an important area of health over which children can have control and for which they can take responsibility.

Give each child a copy of the activity sheet. Invite them to cut out the body and stick her in their book or on a piece of paper. Underneath, they should write three headings – *Teeth*, *Hair* and *Body*. The six items at the bottom of the sheet should be cut up and stuck under the appropriate heading.

Extension

Some children may like to write a sentence for each item e.g. 'I clean my teeth with a toothbrush twice a day.'

When the body is clean, invite the children to design some new clothes for her.

Ideas for SEN Support

It may be more appropriate for some children to stick the six items around the body and then draw arrows to the body parts.

Healthy teeth

This activity is intended to allow the children to think about what is required to keep their teeth healthy and clean. It will help them to categorise what is good for their teeth and what is bad for their teeth.

Try and make a collection of literature from your local dentist and use these as a starting point. Look at the pictures. What do they show us? If you have confident readers they can pick out key words to do with teeth e.g. *calcium, fluoride*. If possible show the children a tube of toothpaste and look at its contents. Ask the children to feel their teeth with their tongue. Can they identify different types of teeth in their mouths? Let some children try to explain these differences – some may be brave enough to draw them!

Using a board or piece of paper, brainstorm all the ways that we can look after our teeth. What would happen if we did not take care of our teeth? Discuss the fact that they will lose one set of teeth as a natural process.

Make a list of things/foods that are good for the teeth e.g. fruit, milk, brushing teeth, and things/food that are bad for the teeth e.g. sugar, foods that contain sugar.

Give each child a copy of the activity sheet. Explain that you want them to think of three things that are good for their teeth and three things that are bad for their teeth. Good things should be drawn in the ovals, bad things should be drawn in the squares.

Extension

Children could design a toothpaste container to promote healthy teeth. Try and encourage them to include some of the language included in the introduction.

Ideas for SEN Support

Reduce the amount of choices to be made by the child or, if an adult is available, you might like to do this activity as a group on a large scale so that the children are completing one big picture each to contribute to a group display.

Growing older

This activity gives the children the opportunity to think about the process of growing from young to old. It examines how people's needs change during this time.

Divide the children into small groups and give each group three pictures cut out from a magazine – a baby, a teenager and an old person. Ask them to stick these pictures on a piece of card, with the youngest at one end and the oldest at the other end. The final picture should be stuck in the middle. Return as a whole class to compare results.

Now ask what different types of things these people need to survive, and collect ideas on the board. Try to convey the idea that needs change throughout life but often we end up needing similar things in our old age to those we needed when we were very young.

Give each child a copy of the activity sheet, which will extend this idea by inviting them to put six people in the correct order.

Extension

Some children may like to return to the pictures from magazines and find others to complete their time-line. They may also like to write or draw things that people need at different ages beside each picture.

Ideas for SEN Support

It may help some children to concentrate on the concept of old and young. A sorting game with animals can help with this – kitten/cat, puppy/dog, chick/hen, baby/old person.

Grub the Germ

This activity encourages the children to think about what germs are and how they can be spread. It gives the children the opportunity to think about things they can do to prevent the spread of germs and how they can encourage others to do the same.

Write the word GERM on a board or large piece of paper. Ask if anybody knows what it means. Take several suggestions and discuss these. Talk about what these germs do to us if they are spread e.g. if somebody has got a bad cold and does not use a tissue, what could happen?

Talk about the conditions in which germs like to grow e.g. warm, moist areas.

Make a list of or brainstorm the ways germs can be spread: through the air, on our hands, through our saliva. Take each one in turn and talk about the ways we can prevent the spread of germs e.g. germs on hands can be removed by washing hands.

Give each child a copy of the activity sheet. Talk about the need to destroy the central character. Emphasise that it is the responsibility of each of us to destroy the germs that surround us. In order to destroy the germ the children have to fill in ways of how to do this e.g. wash your hands after going to the toilet. As each child completes the sheet and destroys the germ, you might wish to give them a seal of 'GERM-FREE ZONE' and cross out the central character.

Extension

Using the word GERM, the children might like to think of a word or picture to represent each letter e.g. G – Give a tissue to somebody who is sneezing.

Ideas for SEN Support

You may wish to have the statements written out on card which they have to match up with a further statement, e.g. IF YOU SNEEZE – USE A TISSUE.

Design a label

This activity is intended to provide the children with information on how germs can be controlled or killed using manufactured products.

If possible, show the children a collection of labels from household cleaners that clean and kill germs. Obviously this needs to be carefully handled and emphasis placed on the fact that these products should be used by adults only.

If it is not possible to obtain labels, make a collection of some phrases that are contained on well-known brand bottles.

Ask the children
• Why is it important to use products that kill germs?
• Where would you use these cleaning products?
• What would you need to do to protect yourself whilst using them?

Give each child a copy of the activity sheet. Explain that you want them to design a bottle label that would make you want to buy the product. Discuss the need for pictures to show germs being killed, or a clean environment if you feel that the former is too gruesome! Share some examples of what their product could be called so that the children have a bank to work from.

Extension

Some children might wish to think of a catchy slogan to add to their product, e.g. GIVE THE GERMS A DRINK – WASH THEM DOWN THE SINK.

Ideas for SEN Support

You might wish to give some children a bottle with a product name already added which they could then illustrate.

ACTIVITY SHEET 25

name ....

Parts of the body

Fill in the correct parts of the body.

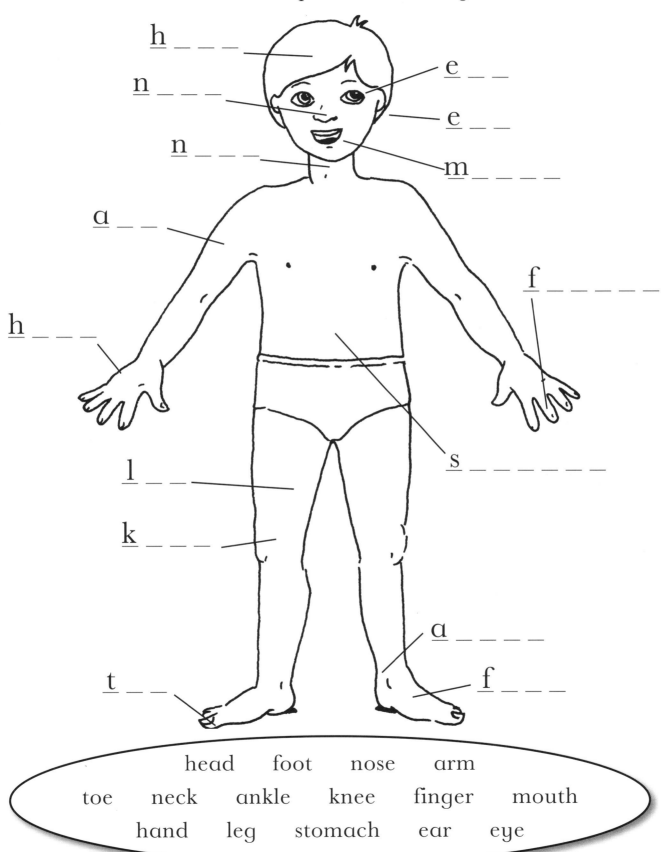

h _ _ _ _

n _ _ _ _

n _ _ _

e _ _ _

e _ _

m _ _ _ _ _

a _ _ _

h _ _ _

f _ _ _ _ _

s _ _ _ _ _ _

l _ _ _

k _ _ _

a _ _ _ _ _

f _ _ _

t _ _

head   foot   nose   arm

toe   neck   ankle   knee   finger   mouth

hand   leg   stomach   ear   eye

name ....

Can you keep clean?

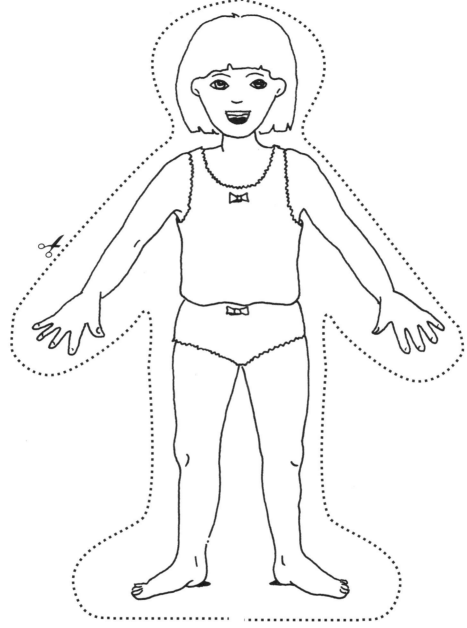

toothpaste	soap	flannel
all white	soap	
shampoo	comb	toothbrush
Kids SHAMPOO		

name ....

Healthy teeth

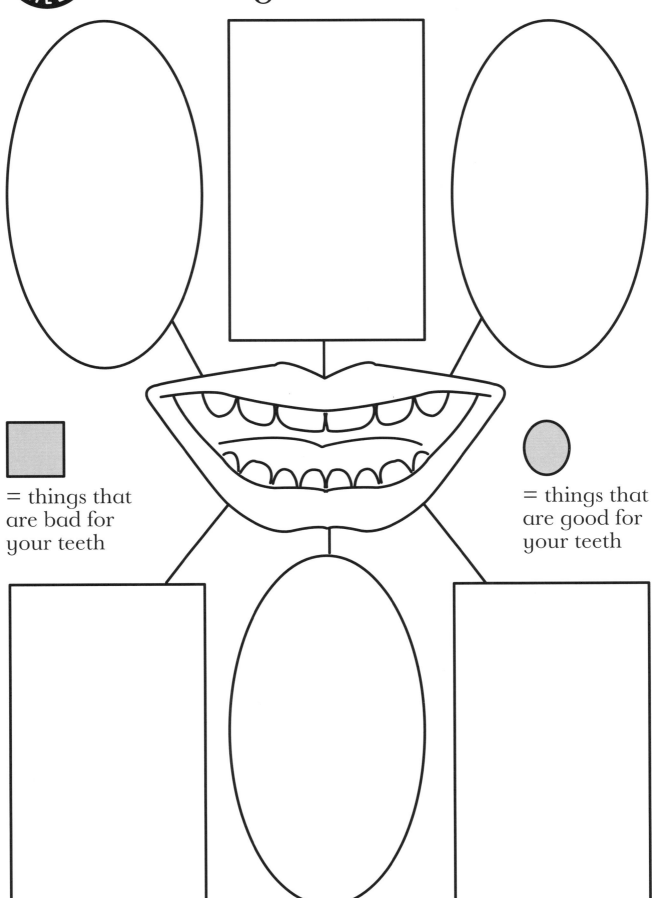

= things that are bad for your teeth

= things that are good for your teeth

name ....

Growing older

Cut out the pictures and stick them in the right order!

	6
	5
	4
	3
	2
	1

ACTIVITY 29 SHEET

Grub the germ

Help to destroy GRUB – help to stop the spread of germs…

. . . .
. . . .
. . . .
. . . .
. . . .

. . . .
. . . .
. . . .
. . . .
. . . .

. . . .
. . . .
. . . .
. . . .

name . . . .

Design a label

Design a label to show that this bottle
KILLS GERMS!

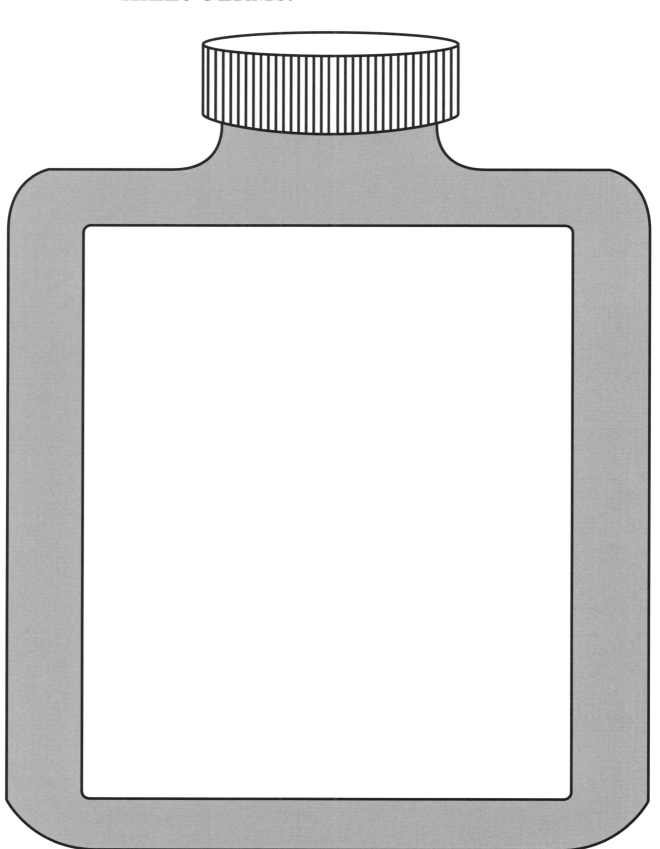

Fill the first aid box

This activity gives the children an awareness that medicines and pills can be harmful if they are not taken properly. It helps them to realise that adults should supervise the taking of prescribed drugs and that all dangerous medicines and first aid items should be kept away from young children.

As a starting point, ask the school nurse to come to talk to the children. Ask her to show the children the type of things that a first aid kit may contain. Use it as an opportunity to discuss the dangers of some of these items. Also discuss rules for taking prescribed drugs, both at home and in school.

Give each child a copy of the activity sheet, ensuring that you read it through with them before they begin. Invite the children to draw any items that may be dangerous, or to write their names, inside the first aid box.

Extension

Some children may like to draw large versions of the dangerous items for a wall display entitled 'Danger – Beware!'.

Ideas for SEN Support

Spend some time discussing why the items could be dangerous. Are they sharp? Could they be poisonous? Invite the children to draw red arrows from the dangerous items into the box and to circle the safe items in green.

Safety jigsaw

This activity helps to make the children aware of all the potentially dangerous situations around them in their own homes. It encourages them to think about ways of keeping safe and highlights the dangers of household products, appliances and fireworks.

Ask the children to work in small mixed ability groups. Give each group a copy of the activity sheet and ask them to cut up the jigsaw so that there are five pictures and five pieces of writing. Invite the groups to pair the jigsaw pieces up correctly and to stick them on a piece of card.

When the groups have completed the task, ask them to gather together and, using a large photocopy of the activity sheet, ask each group to supply one of the answers. Use each answer as an opportunity to discuss the dangers of the situation and ways in which they could be safer. Who is responsible for each? Why?

Extension

Invite some children to look at the different dangers that they may come across such as

- dangers at home
- dangers on the road
- dangers from water
- dangers from strangers
- dangers from medicine and drugs
- dangers from bullies

Ask them to discuss each type of danger and then to put them in order with the one that they think is the greatest danger to them personally first.

Ideas for SEN Support

Give each member of the group the five pictures. Read the captions to the group and ask them to give you the correct pictures. Spend plenty of time discussing each picture and collect words from them such as *hot, pan, burn, fall* etc. Using one picture, they may like to write one sentence to go with it e.g. 'The pan is hot.' 'I may fall on my toys.'

People who keep us safe

This activity introduces the children to the people in the community who keep us safe. It gives them the opportunity to meet and talk to one or more of these people.

As a starting point invite local police officers, fire fighters and the school crossing warden to come into the classroom to talk to the children about their jobs. Invite the children to ask any questions that they might have. Use the discussion as an opportunity to clearly outline ways in which the children can keep themselves safer in the home and on the streets.

In a follow-up session give each child a copy of the activity sheet to complete. Invite the children to choose one or more of the people who keep us safe. On a fresh piece of paper they can extend their work: 'This is a _____. He keeps us safe by _____' etc.

Extension

Invite the children to think which of the jobs they would like to do when they are older. They may like to write a little about *why* they would like to do this job. Alternatively use this as a circle time activity – "I would like to be a _____ because _____."

Ideas for SEN Support

Fill in two activity sheets before the teaching session and cut then up so that the pictures and labels are separate. Let the children take it in turns to pick up a picture and a label. If they match they can keep them, if not, they put them back. Encourage the children to read out the name on the label each time.

Bike safety

This activity is intended to promote bike safety. It encourages children who have bikes to think about what is needed for their safety. It gives those who do not have a bike an opportunity to think about the accessories needed for riding a bike.

Ask the class who owns a bike and pose the following questions:

* Where do you ride your bike?
* Who is with you when you ride your bike?
* What do you wear when you ride your bike?

Using a large diagram (or real bike), name and label all the key features of a standard bike. Ask the children what parts of the bike need to be checked regularly – brakes, tyres, lights. What would happen if they were not checked regularly?

Using a child as a model, discuss what type of clothing should be worn to help to protect the child – helmet, reflective armbands etc. Real accessories should be used if possible.

Give each child a copy of the activity sheet. Tell them that they have to label the bike using the words discussed earlier. On the road signs they can write or draw examples of how to keep safe on a bike.

Extension

The children can choose another leisure time activity e.g. rollerblades, and suggest all the safety features needed.

Ideas for SEN Support

Large road signs can be prepared and the children can choose one safety aspect to name and illustrate.

The accident

This activity gives the children the opportunity to think about the reasons for road safety. It gives them a clear message that cars can hurt you very badly. It will encourage them to play safely where there is no traffic.

As an outside activity take the children to look at a busy main road and then a quiet side road. Discuss the dangers of crossing both types of roads. Dangers on a busy road are more obvious but make the children aware that quiet roads also have dangers e.g. parked cars and fast-approaching cars. Discuss safe places for them to play e.g. gardens and parks, explaining *why* they should keep away from traffic.

Back in the classroom, give each child a copy of the activity sheet. You may wish to do this as a piece of shared writing with the whole class. The children should write one or two sentences to go with each picture if they are able.

Extension

Some children may like to design road safety posters to convey information like 'Cars can kill'. Their posters can be displayed around the school.

Ideas for SEN Support

Cut the activity sheet into four pictures so that the children can put them in sequence. Encourage them to tell the story orally – prompting them with appropriate questions. The children may like to stick them in order and have a go at writing one word to go with each picture.

Road safety song

This activity reinforces the rules for basic road safety in the form of a poem or a song. Children often find it easier to remember things when they are presented in rhyme.

Read or sing 'Keep Yourself Safe!' to the children. You will find that it fits well to the tune of 'If I were a butterfly'. At the end ask the children if they can remember any of the road safety rules from it. Talk about each rule, using it as an opportunity to explain what could happen if they didn't follow the rule.

Teach the children the chorus part of 'Keep Yourself Safe.' Simple actions can be added – pointing to left then right and looking all around etc. When the children are confident with the chorus, introduce the two verses. It may be easier to split the children into three groups so that they are responsible for only part of each verse.

'Keep Yourself Safe' can be used as part of an assembly so that other children in the school can learn from its message too.

Extension

Invite the children to use a variety of sound from pitched instruments, non-pitched instruments and ordinary objects to illustrate an accident on the road. You may wish to help them first by giving them some ideas e.g.

- cymbals – the point of collision
- rattles and maracas – people walking or running
- tambours and tambourines – doors slamming
- recorders and whistles – the screeching of breaks etc.

The children can work either in groups or as a whole class with the class teacher orchestrating the sequence.

Ideas for SEN Support

This activity is suitable for all abilities.

name . . . .

Fill the first aid box

Which items need to be locked safely away?

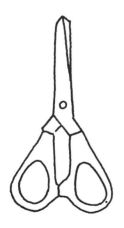

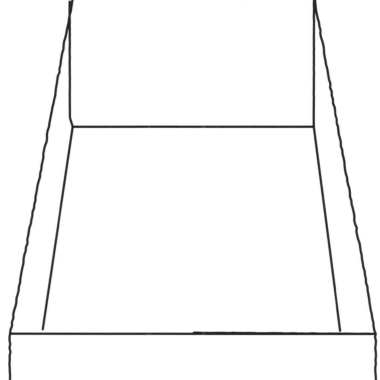

FIRST AID

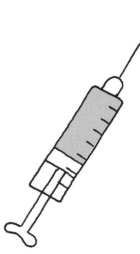

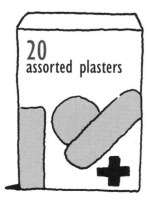

20 assorted plasters

TABLETS

COTTON WOOL

56

name ....

Safety jigsaw

Cut out the pieces and pair them up correctly.

	The girl is too near to the fireworks.
	Toys have been left all over the stairs.
	The cupboard containing bleach has been left open.
	The saucepan has its handle sticking out.
	The hot iron has been left out.

name ....

People who keep us safe

Fill in the names of the people who keep us safe.

p _ _ _ _ _

p _ _ _ _ _

_ _ _ _

p _ _ _ _ _ _ _ _

f _ _ _

_ _ _ _ _ _ _

c _ _ _ _ _ _ _

_ _ _ _ _

t _ _ _ _ _ _

fire fighter   crossing warden   parent

police lady   policeman   teacher

ACTIVITY 34 SHEET

name . . . .

Bike safety

Label the bike and think of some ways to keep yourself safe.

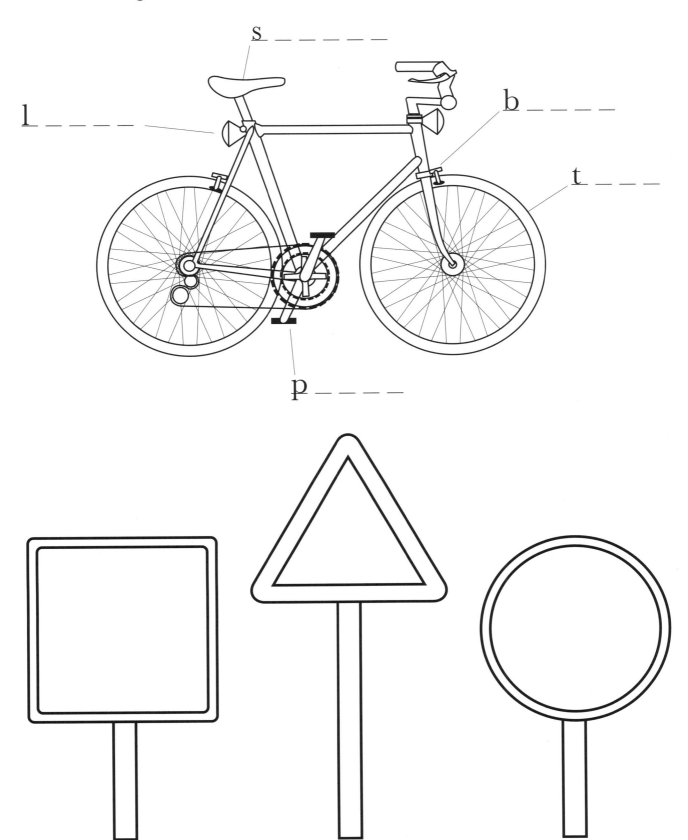

s _ _ _ _ _ _

l _ _ _ _ _

b _ _ _ _

t _ _ _

p _ _ _ _

name ....

The accident

Write a sentence about each picture. Use the words at the bottom to help you.

....

....

....

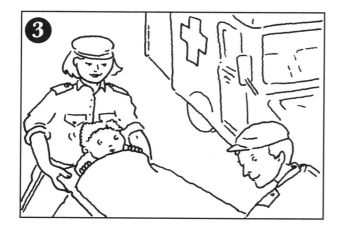

....

....

....

running   ball   road   car   bump   ambulance

hospital   hurt   leg   plaster   crutches   alive

Road safety song

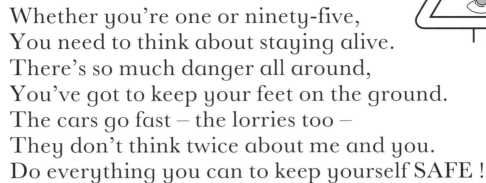

Keep Yourself Safe!

Whether you're one or ninety-five,
You need to think about staying alive.
There's so much danger all around,
You've got to keep your feet on the ground.
The cars go fast – the lorries too –
They don't think twice about me and you.
Do everything you can to keep yourself SAFE !

You must look to the left, you must look to the right,
You must wait 'till there aren't any cars in sight .
Do everything you can to keep yourself SAFE!

When you need to cross the road
Put your brain into thinking mode.
Find a crossing if you can –
Or wait for help from a lollipop man.
Play your games in the local park –
And don't stay out when it's nearly dark.
Do everything you can to keep yourself SAFE!

You must look to the left, you must look to the right,
You must wait 'till there aren't any cars in sight.
Do everything you can to keep yourelf SAFE!
EVERYTHING YOU CAN DO TO KEEP
   YOURSELF SAFE!

Clare Rowland

Recipe for a friend

This activity is intended to allow the children to think of the traits that are needed to make a good friend. It encourages them to think about why they choose certain people to play with and what kind of qualities they possess themselves.

Ask the children to think of one person who is their friend and think of a word to describe this person. Collect these ideas on the board or a large piece of paper. There will be repetition but this is necessary to show the popularity of some traits. Ask why some things are more important than others. Ask the children to look at the traits and evaluate if these traits apply to themselves. They should realise that if they are friends to others they too will show these traits.

Show examples of simple recipes that contain four to six ingredients. Discuss the idea that recipes require more of one ingredient than others. Using a recipe as a frame, tell the children that they are going to substitute their traits for ingredients in order to make their own good friend.

Give each child a copy of the activity sheet. Explain to them that they are going to choose the most important ingredients needed to make a good friend. Remind them of the differing amounts of some ingredients. They should write these on the parts of the body – cut it out and rearrange in their book or on a piece of paper.

Extension

The children can write a recipe that would describe them as a person and as they see themselves as a friend.

Ideas for SEN Support

As a supported group the children should identify one trait that they feel is important. These could contribute to one whole recipe and one person.

Are we all the same?

This activity enables the children to identify the similarities and differences between people. It encourages them to respect the differences between people and thus helps them to develop good relationships.

For homework ask the children to find out

1 Where they were born *or*
2 Which religion they belong to

They may like to bring in pictures of themselves as babies or important artefacts for their religion.

As a class, discuss the differences and similarities between them. Concentrate on physical appearance to begin with. How many children have brown hair? How many children have blue eyes? What colour is their skin? Use this as an opportunity to discuss the importance of the type of person we are inside. Does it really matter what we look like? Does how we behave matter more?

Give each child a copy of the activity sheet and invite them to complete the first row on the chart with their own name and their own details. For each section they should draw a small picture and colour it correctly and also write their answer. You may wish to collect the vocabulary they will need on the board or a large piece of paper. It may also help to to give any religious symbols that are needed.

When each child has completed their own details they can move on to filling in the chart for the others in their group.

Extension

The information that the children collect could be used as a starting point for a display 'All About Us'. They could use the data they have collected to produce a range of charts, diagrams and graphs.

Ideas for SEN Support

Some children may wish to concentrate on hair, eye and skin colour only. They can use pictorial answers in their chart.

What do we like?

This activity is intended as a follow up to Activity Sheet 38 – *Are we all the same?* It continues to examine similarities and differences between the children but this time focuses on likes and dislikes. Once again it encourages them to respect these differences.

As a circle time activity ask the children to complete 'My favourite food is…', 'my favourite T.V. programme is…'. Use this as an opportunity to discuss the fact that we all have different likes and dislikes and that everyone is entitled to their own opinion. As different ideas come from the class, collect the vocabulary on the board or a large piece of paper.

Give each child a copy of the activity sheet and invite them to complete the first row with their own name and their own details. If they have completed Activity Sheet 7 – *Like or lump it*, they may wish to use it to help them. They can also use the words you collected earlier.

When they have completed their own details they can, again, fill in the chart for the rest of their group with the pictures and words.

Extension

Ak the children to think about friends they may have outside school. Why are they friends with them? Do we always make friends with similar people with similar interests?

Ideas for SEN Support

Some children may find it easier to work with only one other child and to compare their favourite things. Use it as an opportunity to reinforce the point that we should always respect other people's differences.

A star friend

This activity allows the children to think about their special friends and think of reasons why they are so special. It should reflect on the fact that different people respect and like different things about people.

As the teacher, tell the children the name of one of your friends. Put this name on the board or a large piece of paper and then write

' _____ is a star friend because _____ '

Give at least three different reasons e.g. he is good at football, he makes me laugh, he has a good singing voice.

Repeat this activity with a few children from the class. Write down the reasons given by the rest of the class in order to build up a word bank.

Give each child a copy of the activity sheet (this should be copied on to card). Tell them that you want them to choose one person who is a star friend to them. They will have to draw this person in the centre of the sheet. In the stars they should write the reasons why this person is a star friend. When they have finished they should cut the stars out. These stars then need to be presented to their star friend either at the end of this session or at another time.

Extension

The children can use the information on the stars to write a short description of their star friend, using complete sentences.

Ideas for SEN Support

The children should be encouraged to draw the picture of their star friend. Help should be given by an adult to those who have difficulty with writing or spelling.

Who cares?

This activity gives the children the chance to think about practical ways that they can care for their family and friends.

Photocopy an enlarged copy of the activity sheet to work from with the whole class. Open the discussion by asking the children who cares for them and in what ways. Examine the question 'Is caring a two-way process?' Discuss the importance that caring behaviour has as part of good relationships.

Ask the children for examples of ways in which they can care for their families and friends. You may need to help them with a few ideas first.

- Giving mum a hug and saying thank you
- Helping dad to fold up the ironing
- Giving a bottle to a baby brother or sister
- Playing in the garden with the dog
- Helping a friend with homework etc.

For each example you are given, draw a small picture inside the heart to represent the caring behaviour (e.g. a bottle, a dog, book with pencil etc) and write the name of the person it applies to.

When the children are familiar with the format, give them each a copy of the activity sheet and invite them to think of six of their own examples.

Extension

Using their finished activity sheets as prompts, invite the children to tell the rest of their group how they are going to care for each person that they have chosen. They may like to report back after a week to discuss how they have managed to show that they care in practical ways.

Ideas for SEN Support

This activity is suitable for all abilities. However, some children may benefit from extra suggestions from an adult.

People who care for us

This activity is intended to allow the children the opportunity to think of all the people in their lives who care for them. This should reinforce the fact that caring is a two-way process and is something that we should thank people for.

Invite the children to sit in a circle and in turn ask them for an example of one person who has done something caring for them that day, e.g. 'My mum has cared for me today by kissing me before she left me.' Try to distinguish between caring and helping.

Ask the children to think of all the people in their lives who they feel care for them. Make a list of these on the board or large piece of paper. Then ask

- Why do these people care for us?
- How do we know that these people care for us?
- What would happen if these people didn't care for us?

Discuss how we sometimes acknowledge that these people care for us (buying presents, saying thank you, sending cards etc.) and why it is important to do so.

Give the children a copy of the activity sheet. Tell them that you want them to think of all the people who care for them. These people will be written in the petals, and reasons given if the children are confident writers.

Extension

The children can cut the flower out and on the reverse they can write 'These are the people I care for.' and fill in the petals.

The flowers can then be hung as mobiles.

Ideas for SEN Support

Instead of writing a reason, the children can draw the people and write their names.

name . . . .

Recipe for a friend

Fill in the ingredients needed for a good friend.
Cut out and create that person!

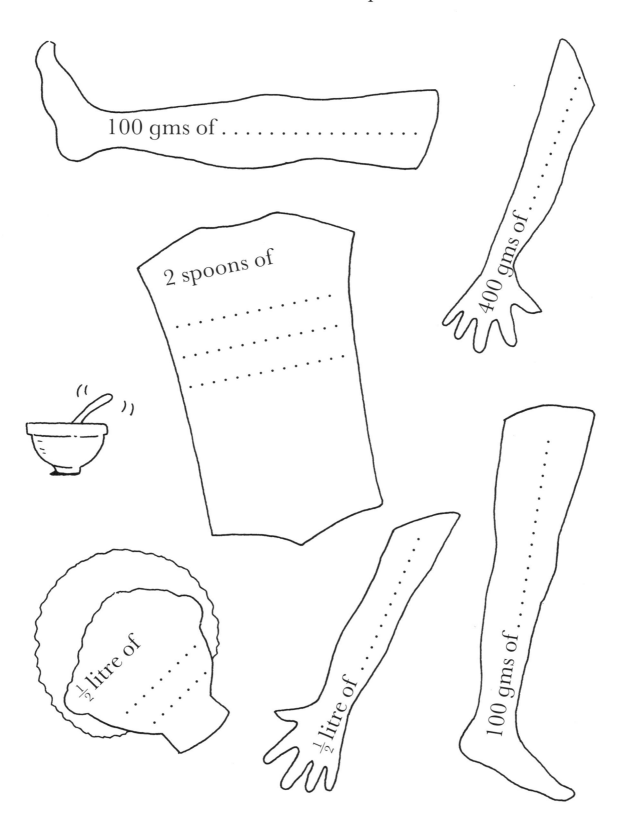

100 gms of . . . .

400 gms of . . . .

2 spoons of

. . . .

. . . .

. . . .

½ litre of . . . .

½ litre of . . . .

100 gms of . . . .

name . . . .

Are we all the same?

Fill in the chart for all the children in your group.

	1	2	3	4	5
Birth place					
Religion					
Skin colour					
Eye colour					
Hair colour					
Name	❶	❷	❸	❹	❺

What do we like?

Fill in the chart for all the children in your group.

Name	Favourite food	Favourite t.v. show	Favourite pop group	Favourite colour	Favourite pastime
❶					
❷					
❸					
❹					
❺					

name ....

A star friend

Draw your star friend in the middle.

Write why they are your star friend in the stars.

Who cares?

name ....

name ....

People who care for us

Name or draw the people who care for you in the petals.

These people care for
ME

Tease or bully?

This activity allows the children the opportunity to think about and discuss the different types of teasing and bullying. It should establish the fact that it is important to tell somebody if they feel they are being bullied.

Invite the children to sit in a circle. Tell the children that they are going to look at ways that children are teased and bullied at school. Have a covered box prepared with some statements for the children to read out and discuss e.g.

- She took my toy and ran off with it.
- He kicked me when nobody was looking.
- She made me give her one of my sweets.
- He said he's not my friend.
- She said she would get her big brother to hit me.

Pass the box around the circle and at appropriate times tell the children to stop. Wherever the box stops, ask that child to pick one piece of paper out of the box and read the statement on it. They may like to ask the children either side of them to help them read it.

For each statement ask the children

- Where might this happen?
- Why does it happen?
- What should you do about it/who could you tell?
- Has this happened to anybody here?

Make a list of the resolutions on the board or a large piece of paper as the statements are discussed. Explain to the children that they are going to work in small groups – these should be mixed ability.

Show them a copy of the activity sheet, explain that they need to cut up the statements and put them into a box. In a similar way they are to pass the box around the group and each child should take a statement to read. Again they can gain help from children either side of them. As a group they should discuss the statement, trying to establish why it happens and what they can do about it. Each group should report back on one statement to the rest of the class.

Extension

The children could try dramatising a few of the examples or creating their own situations which show evidence of teasing and bullying, as well as the resolution.

Ideas for SEN Support

This activity should be done in groups of mixed ability.

Problem page

This activity is intended to allow the children the opportunity to look more carefully at how problems of teasing or bullying can be tackled. It allows the children the chance to consider various dilemmas and offer advice to their friends on how and where they can get help.

Present a problem to the children which has a definite answer, e.g. 'I want to read my book but it's too dark.' Ask the children what advice they would give (turn on the lights). Define the terms *problem* and *advice* to help the children identify the difference. Present a problem that does not have such a definite answer e.g. 'Somebody keeps calling me names. I don't like it but they won't stop it.' Encourage all the different pieces of advice that the children might give and indicate which piece of advice you would follow. Develop the idea that sometimes they might have to offer advice to their friends. They must first of all establish what is right or wrong in the situation and then offer advice accordingly.

Give a copy of the activity sheet to the children and read through the two problems which are presented. Try and establish whether the problems constitute bullying. Tell the children that you want them to think of how they would respond to the problem. A few children could read out their responses to the rest of the class to see how they differ.

You may like to change the problems to meet the needs of your children if bullying is a problem in your class at the time.

Extension

Some children could try and establish a list of all the types of bullying that they are faced with. Alongside this they could try to write all the resolutions that they feel would be the most effective.

Ideas for SEN Support

As a small group and with adult help the children could choose one problem which they want to respond to – the adult could act as the scribe.

Bullying wordsearch

This activity is intended to show the children that there are different kinds of teasing and bullying that they may come across. It extends the children's vocabulary on the theme of bullying.

Give each child a copy of the activity sheet. Read the words with them, ensuring that they understand the meaning of each word. Discuss how this bullying behaviour might make them feel, giving examples for each word. Also discuss how they might help someone who is being subjected to teasing or bullying.

Invite the children to complete the activity sheet by finding all the bullying words and then colouring them red. You may wish to draw their attention to the fact that all the words have 'ing' at the end of them. This should make their search a little easier!

Extension

Invite the more able children to use their dictionaries to look up and note the precise meanings of the words listed. Some children may like to list other types of bullying behaviour or work on drama sketches which show bullies in action and the effect they have.

Ideas for SEN Support

Some of the vocabulary used in the wordsearch may be too difficult for the children. They can be paired with a more able child or put in a group with an adult to supervise. Use the 'ing' ending and invite the children to collect simple rhyming words e.g. *cooking – looking, booking – saying, playing – falling, calling* etc.

Pam and the bullies

This activity highlights different types of teasing and bullying. It enables the children to think about different ways of dealing with bullying.

Enlarge the activity sheet and use it with the whole class to discuss 'Pam and the bullies'. Cover up the sentences at the bottom of the sheet. Look at each picture in turn, asking the children for their interpretations of what is happening in the picture. Explore questions such as "What might they be saying?" "How may they be feeling?" The final question "What should Pam do?" can be used as an opportunity for the children to put forward their own ideas for ways to stop bullying.

Give each child a copy of the activity sheet. Invite them to cut up the six pieces of text and to stick the correct piece of text with each picture. If they are able, ask them to answer the final question in their own words.

Extension

Some children may like to make up their own bullying story in the same format – six pictures and six short pieces of writing. Invite them to cut their stories up and give them to others in their group to sequence correctly.

Ideas for SEN Support

Give each child the six pictures to sequence correctly. The children may also like to have one picture and then sequence single words to form a sentence to go with it e.g. 'Jill and Ben took her crisps.'

Bully or not?

This activity gives the children the opportunity to consider their perceptions of how bullies may look. It should reinforce the idea that outward appearances are not always an accurate indication of inner qualities.

On the board or large piece of paper prepare two large outlines or silhouettes of a child's head and shoulders – entitle them BULLY and NOT BULLY. Cut out a selection of pictures of people from magazines which portray a mixture of gender, age, sex and ethnicity. You should also prepare a brief character study for each person e.g. Jason is a kind man who always helps his friends, Rachel often laughs at her friend when she makes a mistake. Keep the character details to yourself for the time being.

In turn ask the children if the person that you hold up is a bully or not and ask them to explain their choices. Place the person on the silhouette which indicates whether the children think they are a BULLY or NOT BULLY. At the end of the activity tell the children if they are right or not by reading out your prepared character studies.

Discuss the fact that it is difficult to tell if somebody is a bully from just physical appearances and that it is wrong to make assumptions based on this alone. Make sure that you recap on the traits that make a bully with the whole class.

Give each child a copy of the activity sheet. Explain why the outline has no features or defining characteristics. Using the words around the silhouette, invite the children to cut out the traits that they think make a bully and then to stick them onto the silhouette.

Extension

Some children may like to draw a picture of Betty the Bully or Billy the Bully on a separate piece of paper. Invite the more able to write a few sentences below their picture to explain why Betty or Billy is a bully e.g. Betty takes my sweets, Billy calls me names etc.

Ideas for SEN Support

The children should be given additional help to read through the traits. You could help them to eliminate the ones not needed so that they can simply cut out and stick on what is left.

Beat the Bullies game

This activity offers the children practical ways to help them deal with bullying. It reinforces the fact that bullying is wrong and encourages them to have the confidence to BEAT THE BULLIES.

As a whole class ask the children if they can think of any ways to stop bullying behaviour or any actions that might stop someone from being bullied. List their suggestions on the board or a large piece of paper. Make sure that you include the strategies on the *Beat the bullies game* i.e.

- Get help
- Ignore them
- Walk away
- Tell an adult
- Be confident

Invite the children to work in groups of three. Give each group a copy of the activity sheet, if possible enlarged to A3 size beforehand. Each player will need a coloured counter and each group will need a dice.

Play commences with the roll of the dice, the players moving their counters accordingly and following the instructions on the game. The winner is the player who reaches the finish first.

Extension

Some children may like to design posters 'BEAT THE BULLIES – WALK AWAY' or 'BEAT THE BULLIES – JUST IGNORE THEM' etc. Finished posters could be displayed around the school to spread the message to other children.

Ideas for SEN Support

You may wish an adult to supervise one group to help the children who have difficulties with turn-taking or who are unable to read the text. As a follow-up activity invite the children to demonstrate how they would deal with bullying behaviour with the adult in the role as the bully!

Tease or bully?

He pinched my crisps.

She wouldn't let me play.

He called me smelly.

They won't talk to me.

She pushed me.

He laughs at me when I read.

name ....

Problem page

What advice would you give to these people?

? ? ?

A boy in my class keeps calling me names. He kicks me when nobody is looking and he steals my sweets.

....
....
....
....
....
....

Some people in my class tease me when I wear my glasses. I've tried reading without glasses but it hurts.

? ? ?

....
....
....
....
....

name . . . .

Bullying wordsearch

Can you find the bullying words?

a	m	b	j	p	c	h	i	r	b	u	e	v	g	f	w
n	l	o	a	k	b	q	t	s	a	a	z	d	y	n	x
b	f	t	e	a	s	i	n	g	i	j	p	p	q	a	r
o	c	d	e	h	n	g	k	m	l	s	u	t	v	m	u
w	s	z	a	x	y	h	b	j	e	g	s	c	k	e	o
q	c	r	u	s	t	o	p	f	i	h	h	d	l		m
k	a	j	f	h	m	r	d	v	c	b	i	x	z	c	y
i	r	g	l	e	f	i	g	h	t	i	n	g	w	a	a
h	i	o	q	p	r	n	s	u	t	y	g	v	z	l	a
g	n	c	b	d	e	g	h	j	p	s	t	x	w	l	z
n	g	i	o	f	m	l	k	v	u	q	r	w	x	i	y
a	c	f	e	g	d	h	k	j	i	m	l	o	q	n	r
b	t	h	r	e	a	t	e	n	i	n	g	n	p	g	s
t	x	w	a	e	f	g	j	k	l	q	r	s	x	b	c
y	u	g	a	n	g	i	n	g		u	p	t	a	y	d
v	z	d	c	b	i	h	p	n	m	v	w	u	e	f	z

ganging up

fighting

pushing

scaring

teasing

ignoring

threatening

name calling

Pam and the bullies

At play time they called her names. They took her crisps.	"Tell teacher," said her friend Sam. What should Pam do?
Jill and Ben sat on her table. They always ignored her.	They scribbled on her work. The teacher didn't see.
It was Monday morning. Pam didn't want to go to school.	"Off you go!" said her mum. Pam was feeling very sad.

ACTIVITY 47 SHEET

name . . . .

Bully or not?

| gives me sweets | takes my sweets |
| helps me with my work | says nasty things about my family |

| pinches me and pulls my hair | leaves me out of the game |
| calls me names | smiles at me |

78

name ....

Beat the Bullies game

A game for 3 players

You will need: a counter for each player
a dice

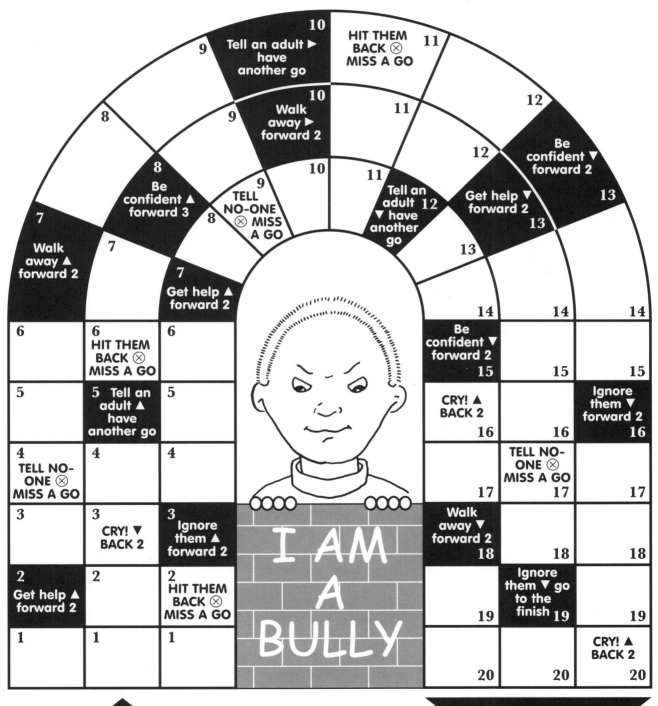

Resources: Fiction

Feeling Good
The Tough Princess – M. Weddell (Walker Books)
Funny Stories To Make You Laugh – M. Rosen (Kingfisher)
Could You Leave The Light On? – A. de Bode and C. Broere (Evans)
No Matter What – Debi Gliori (Bloomsbury)
Good Day Bad Day – Kathryn White (Oxford)

Belonging to a Family
My New Sister – Rebecca Hunter (Evans)
My New Dad – Rebecca Hunter (Evans)
My First Pet – Rebecca Hunter (Evans)
You Will Always Be My Dad – A. de Bode and C. Broere (Evans)
My Mum's a Window Cleaner – B. Gilan (Methuen)
My New Mum and Me – B. Wright (Blackwell)
The Tigger Movie Story Book – Disney (Ladybird)

Staying Healthy
The Giant Jam Sandwich – J.V. Lord (Piccolo)
Dad's Diet – B. Gunber – (Arncliffe)
Tomorrow I Will Feel Better – A. de Bode and C. Broere (Evans)
The Rascally Cake – Jeanne Willis and Korky Pam (Puffin)
My First Visit to Hospital – Rebecca Hunter (Evans)

Keeping Clean
Fungus the Bogey Man – C. Briggs (Hamish Hamilton)

Being Safe
We Can Say No – D. Pithers and S. Greene (Red Fox)

Having Friends
Friends and Brothers – Dick King Smith (Mammoth)

Beating Bullies
It's Always Me They're After – A. de Bode and C. Broere (Evans)
Chicken – A. Gibbons (Dolphin)
Willy the Wimp – A. Brown (Methuen)
Frightened Fred – Peta Coplans (Anderson Press)
The Selfish Crocodile – Faustin Charles and Michael Terry (Bloomsbury)

Resources: Non-fiction

The Big Book of Baby Animals – N. Jones (Dorling Kindersley)
How to Look after Your Rabbit – Colin and Jacqui Hawkins (Walker)
I Love Guinea Pigs – Dick King Smith (Walker)
Looking Into My Body – N. Nelson (Joshua Morris)
How Your Body Works – C.Maynard, J. de Saulles and H.Songhurst (Zig Zag)
If I Didn't Have Elbows – Sandi Toksvig (Zero to Ten)
100 Questions and Answers – Diseases and Medicines – Steve Parker (Puffin)
Why Are All Families Different? – M.Atkinson (Dorling Kindersley)
Rainbows Safety (4 titles) – (Evans)
Rainbows Religion (6 titles) – (Evans)
Family Matters – Julian Powell – (Evans)
Food Matters – Julian Powell – (Evans)
Gangs and Bullies – Rosemary Stones – (Evans)